The Lullaby Effect

The science of singing
to your child

Anita Collins

The Lullaby Effect
The science of singing to your child

First published in Australia by Anita Collins 2018
www.thelullabyeffect.com.au

Prepublication Data Service details available from
The National Library of Australia
ISBN: 978-0-6483539-0-4 (pbk)
ISBN: 978-0-6483539-1-1 (ebk)

Typesetting and design by Publicious Book Publishing
Published in collaboration with Publicious Book Publishing
www.publicious.com.au

Dedication

To my body baby, Little Miss E.

CONTENTS

Introduction

My body and brain babies

"I feel like I'm giving birth to two babies; one with my body and one with my brain!" I said to my PhD supervisor when I was six months' pregnant and about to give an important presentation as part of my PhD in Neuroscience and Music Education at the University of Melbourne.

I vividly remember the day because it was the last day I could officially fly (I don't live in Melbourne). Well, I "failed" my PhD presentation. In reality I didn't fail, but the assessment panel said I needed to do "more work", that I wasn't ready to proceed just yet.

I don't know if I recognised the irony at the time, but not only was I not ready to proceed with my PhD, my brain baby, I wasn't ready (can you ever be?) to proceed with my body baby either. This was my first pregnancy and it didn't matter how much I had read, I felt like I was being sideswiped every day with new experiences and challenges to do with growing a baby. Having these two experiences occurring simultaneously led to one crushing conclusion: "I'm so not ready!"

Why share this with you? As I was writing this book I realised what a unique situation I was in – and when I look back, what a unique opportunity I had been given. I was studying how sound and music changed a child's brain, and here I was with my own little experiment subject. That sounds a little creepy, but now that my daughter is about to turn seven and I have just passed the fourth anniversary of my PhD graduation, the power of the experience has become clearer to me.

It also struck me that the clarity I now have about how babies use sound and music to make sense of their world and how impactful their sound environment is on them came not from running experiments on my daughter and her peers, but from observing how they reacted to, and used, sound and music. I often tried to put myself into their sound world, to listen and be aware of my emotional and physiological reactions. In doing so I found that magical space between my daughter and me, the understanding of what each of us needed, how each of us was feeling, and a sense of growing with her as a person.

It probably sounds like it was all sunshine and rainbows and I guess on balance and in hindsight it was. Any parent knows that sometimes those rainbows seem like distant memories and in the trenches of the baby and toddler years it is just plain hard work.

I used to say life before my daughter was sometimes on a knife edge, as I balanced many different projects in my professional life and was in the habit of saying "what's next?" as soon as I felt like I had mastered my latest challenge. After my daughter was born, that knife became so much sharper and I felt like my hands were covered with soap as I held the knife. My brain and body babies couldn't coexist for very long, so I had to get moving and complete my PhD – the baby that had an end date in terms of my involvement.

A PhD is a mysterious and individual experience but here is my definition of it: it is both a passion project and a tick in the box. You choose a burning question you are passionate about answering. You dive into a pool of research that other people have already done, trying to learn as much as you can in an attempt to find where the question you're passionate about might fit in. At a certain point, you have to emerge from the deep and satisfying pool of intensely interesting research and start ticking boxes.

Sometimes the box ticking is a deeply *un*satisfying part of the process (although several of my researcher friends love this part). You have to design an experiment of some type, do the experiment, make sense of what your experiment found, and then relate it back to what everyone else said before you. Then you need to become the world expert in just one thing; you need to add one new piece of knowledge to the vast database of human understanding.

To me, my brain baby was not that far removed from my body baby. I was passionate about the idea of having a baby, learned as much as I could before she was born, and now daily life with her still feels like one big experiment that I can sometimes make sense of. And in the end, I contribute in part to one new human being in the world who will, I hope, add in some way to the vast database of humanity.

The knowledge I was seeking from this PhD concerned how we as human beings understand music, how we use it to develop our brains and how that development impacts on our lives. Music is often described as organised sound, so I quickly found myself having to understand how we process sound.

I discovered that music in our brains is not just organised sound, it is *all* sound. For example, in a study of one-day-old babies, it was observed that they hear their mother's voice as if it were music. Was my daughter listening to my voice and hearing music? What did this mean for how she was experiencing the voices at day care or when we were at the playground? If her day had a soundtrack, what would it sound like?

This one revelation blew my mind, and it wasn't the only one. The idea that sound is information and that our auditory system never turns off, even when we sleep, made me look at my daughter's daily experiences as an equally rich and damaging environment. Then there was the idea that enrichment of her auditory environment was not all about happy music and emotionally positive voices. To develop her auditory network in a rich way she needed a wide variety of sounds. This meant she needed to hear many voices and sound sources, upset voices and warning tones, and environments that had multiple layers of sound in them.

There was also the idea that from when she was very young she was hearing complex sound environments, like a café or her day care room, as one sound to begin with. Then her brain was working really hard to dissect that one sound into many sounds. Lastly, there was the idea that one of the most important parts of her auditory development was to draw out speech from all the other sounds and that this was one of the first steps in learning how to use language. And this was all happening inside her head without me even knowing!

I started to pay very close attention to all her reactions: where her eyes went when she was in a rich sound environment; when she became agitated to remove herself from sound; her emotional reaction to sound and music, which seemed to vary from week to week, sometimes day to day. As I paid attention to her experiences of sound and music I kept reading research about brain development and music, and my two babies weren't fighting anymore, they were playing and learning together.

My PhD was just the beginning of this journey. Since I let my brain baby go out into the world and got the "Dr" in front of my name I have become more, not less, passionate about this area of research. In the last two years, I have interviewed over 100 researchers in the fields of neuroscience and psychology, across 16 laboratories in four different countries. These researchers use sound and music as a tool to understand how the brain develops and changes from birth into older age. They are passionate people, deeply immersed in their own passionate questions and I feel privileged to have spent time in their world. This book is an opportunity to share with you some of what I learned from them.

I had my own passionate question to answer through my PhD, but it wasn't the question I thought it was. It took me until the very end of my brain baby to see what my passionate question really was. I won't share it with you just yet, but I will. I would first like to open the door for you to the research I find so compelling and fascinating, and gave me a whole host of tools and insights into my daughter's development from a newborn, to her first day at school.

My daughter's brain is about to finish its first period of intense growth, known as the sensitivity period. She is turning seven in less than a month's time and it seems fortuitous to be writing this book at this time in her life and in mine. *The Lullaby Effect* is my way of sharing with you the unique opportunity I was given – having a baby with my body and a baby with my brain – to give new parents a window into the auditory world of your little one.

I will share stories of both my babies and describe some of the experiments I tried and learned from. I will also share with you the science behind the sounds, songs and music that your little one is experiencing in the hope that you too can share in your child's sound world.

As I was writing this book I also thought about the whole host of people who have been part of my daughter's development so far. From the carers and educators at her day care centre, to her wonderful grandparents, to her numerous swimming teachers, they all use sound to help her grow and so this book is for them too.

Take a moment to close your eyes and open your ears; there is a new world out there for you and your little one to explore.

How you can use this book

Fifteen months after my daughter was born, I had a monumental moment – I actually finished reading a book of fiction. I made it through one WHOLE book. I hope some of you are nodding your heads right now, feeling both my sense of accomplishment while also asking that bewildering question "what happened to my life?"

It seems ridiculous that something like finishing a book I was reading entirely for my own pleasure was such a feat, but it was. I had been reading journal papers on brain development and big, thick, scary textbooks on research methods, I was balancing two jobs and nurturing my daughter's daily development and amidst all that, reading for pleasure fell off the radar. Sleep was a more attractive option.

That moment was front of mind as I thought about writing this book. I want to give you the satisfaction of finishing sections of the book easily and get out of it what you need. So the chapters are short and the writing style is (hopefully) easy to read. But the researcher in me wanted to back up what I was saying and give you the option of finding out more if you want to.

With that in mind, you will see references to academic citations throughout each chapter. For the researchers or research-oriented people reading this, don't freak out but this is *not* an academic book. Some of the references are to papers that support a statement I have made, others are to point you in the right direction to find out more about a specific area of research. And some references do not necessarily support what I have stated (breathe through it, people).

This book is not meant to be an exhaustive tome of academic research; it is an introduction to the field for those who may not have known about, or had access to, the research. For my academic work, please go to my peer-reviewed, published papers and dive in!

The experience of having a brain and a body baby at the same time also made me curious about the way research is being used to make true and false claims. I read my fair share of articles about everything from nappy rash to sleeping routines and I was struck how often the sentences started with "Research has found that …" or "Scientific research proves …" More alarming was that I tended to believe whatever the article said simply because it was "backed up by science".

Yet the process of doing my PhD taught me that I should be asking more questions when I read those statements. Questions like "how did they come to that conclusion?" "who was in their participant group?" and "what method did they use to come to those results?"

In light of this new source of parental advice, I have also included things to think about when you read the words "A new study has found" at the end of each chapter. Skip this bit if you aren't interested, or flip to it when you read the next research-supported article on Facebook.

Before you start reading, here is a little bit about me:

I began learning clarinet at the age of nine. I thought I might like to be a professional orchestral musician, but after studying at university to do just that I decided it wasn't the life for me. I started out as a very young classroom music teacher at a private boys' school (and I haven't yet left). I am also a teacher of all age groups, and a music conductor of any group I get the opportunity to be in front of (all my years of learning a musical instrument was channelled into being a conductor as soon as I started teaching).

I am also an academic (teaching teachers how to teach) and a researcher (trying to answer perplexing questions), and a creative person who loves writing. I'm particularly fond of a good diagram, I am a talker who likes to see the lights turn on in people's eyes, and I am a listener with all of my body.

I have a private little dream about this book, which I guess isn't private anymore as I'm telling you about it. Have a look at the story that starts Chapter 1 and imagine I am sitting at the table next to a group of young mothers and fathers with their babies. My dream is that I overhear one of them say "I'm reading this book about music and babies' brains and I'm loving it. It is helping me understand how he is understanding the world. You should read it."

Chapter 1

Rockstar parents
Is my voice good enough to sing to my baby?

I do not feel comfortable in a quiet environment. My musically trained brain tends to fill the silence with music inside my head, often multiple soundtracks at once, which can get a little distracting. I have found I do my best work, especially writing, in environments that have a lot of background noise. As I write this I am sitting in a café in Melbourne waiting to attend a conference, and the café noises and the people around me going about their morning make me feel very focused on sharing this chapter with you.

This need for noise all started when I was writing my PhD. I am lucky enough to live in a city that has a gorgeous lake at its centre and I would go to the huge library right next to the lake to read, research and write. But you wouldn't have found me working away in the elegant, ethereally calm and scholarly two-storey reading room in the library. I would be working away outside in the noisy café with the sounds of the coffee machine, with equally scholarly and interesting conversations all around me.

Because the library is situated beside a lake, many new parents would meet at the café there after taking their morning walk with their pram brigade. I couldn't help but overhear their conversations (apologies to everyone I eavesdropped on for my lack of social etiquette but you all have gorgeous little ones). These groups were the brains trust of both new and tried-and-true tricks and ideas to help their little ones grow and thrive.

As I watched and learned from these gatherings, it struck me that this type of sharing is one of the oldest modes of support for child rearing and parenting that we have. It takes a village – and this was their village meeting place.

One conversation I overheard has stayed with me. It taught me something about what we might have lost as 21st century parents. Six mothers with bubs under six months old were chatting, sharing their techniques for swaddling, nappy rash and settling bubs for their midday sleep. One of them was a great source of knowledge, obviously well-read and actively taking every opportunity to assist her son to thrive in his first few months.

She was busily describing the main points of an article she had read about music and a baby's brain. Of course, my ears pricked up. She talked about the importance of talking to her son, singing songs (and she had a list of the "best" ones), moving to music with her son and exposing him to musical instruments and musical play. Mother No. 2 next to her asked, "So which songs do you sing to him?" and Mother No. 1 said quite emphatically, "Oh, I don't sing to him. I can't sing well enough, so I play some opera for him instead."

It took everything I had within me – and I mean everything! – not get out of my chair, go and sit down with this particular pram brigade and start sharing what

I knew about music and singing and their baby's brains. Here I was reading all of this research that pointed to the fact that active music-making is so much more useful than passive music listening. The idea that just listening to Mozart will make our children smarter has been debunked many, many times over[1][2][3].

I have held onto this story; pondered why it made me want to jump up and talk to strangers and why I still want to share with other new parents what I have learned from my body and brain babies. The answer is, *you* are your baby's favourite rockstar (or opera singer – whatever floats your boat), and this is why.

Okay, science stuff coming next

Let's start with Mother No. 1's statement: "I can't sing well enough." I want to break this down to explain two things about singing. Let's start with "I can't sing". I often say to the teachers I work with who make this assumption about themselves, "If you can speak, you can sing." They don't believe me, which is fair enough. But when I delve further into why they believe they can't sing it is usually because someone – a teacher, parent or someone else important in their lives – has said "you can't sing" or "please stop singing, you sound terrible".

The truth is that everyone can sing, but not everyone can sing "well enough" as Mother No. 1 put it, or another way to express it is not everyone can sing "in tune".

So if we can all sing because we all have a voice, what happened to make a significant number of us in adulthood believe we can't sing? When I get the opportunity to speak to parent groups I often like to run a straw poll. I ask the parent group "who thinks they can't sing?" About 70 per cent immediately raise their hand. When I say "keep your hand up if you believe you can't sing because someone told you that you can't sing", most of the hands stay raised; some go up even higher. Why are we so judgemental about another person's, or our own, ability to sing?

The answer is not that we are all expert singers who can't abide poor singing. After all, the "I can't sing" response may well be a super-Western response (thanks to one of my research reviewers for coming up with that one). What would the same people have said before we had the likes of the *X Factor* and *Idol* reality TV shows?

I believe this severe self-judgement could be connected to the deeper and more important role that singing plays in our brain development. At birth, none of us could see very well, we couldn't move our bodies with any control or purpose, and our sense of taste and smell were very underdeveloped, but our hearing was *perfect* (relatively speaking). As an auditory researcher explained to me, our auditory-processing system gathers the largest amount of information of any of our senses, and it never turns off – it is working even when we sleep[4].

One of the most important sources of auditory information is parents' and caregivers' voices. Your baby might not be able to see you clearly for the first three months, but they know who you are through the unique qualities of your voice[5]. In music this is called the tone colour or timbre (pronounced "tamber") of a person's voice. I like to explain it like this:

When you get a phone call – and let's pretend it is not on a mobile phone where you can read the name of the caller – and you hear someone say hello, if it is someone you know really well, then can tell it's them just by the unique timbre of their voice. What's more, you can probably tell by the way they say hello what kind of mood they are in. That's your auditory-processing network in action, gathering information about your world.

Babies are the same. They just haven't had as much experience or, put another way, they haven't had as many "information inputs". So hearing voices that they are familiar with helps them feel safe, familiar and provides some consistency to the vocal sounds they are hearing. The same thing happens to us as parents; we get to know our baby's voice so that when they are playing in the playground we can say, after hearing a single cry, "Okay, that's not my child."

Now, babies are just starting to develop that understanding and they often use their parents' emotional responses to interpret sound. Interesting research has found that parents infuse their speech to babies with very high levels of emotion[6]. You can hear it when a parent speaks directly to their child; it is often in a higher voice with exaggerated differences between the sounds, noticeable differences in how loud the speech is and the rhythm of the words tends to be very regular[7].

In the research this is called "motherese" or "parentese" (AKA baby-talk, or the very posh term is "infant-directed singing") and when I watch the pram brigade mothers speaking to their little ones, it is obvious when they switch from motherese to speaking to other adults. What's more, this is a universal behaviour; people across genders, ages, cultures and parental status noticeably change their voice when they talk to a baby.

Why do we use this exaggerated speech? If you stop for a moment and listen to someone speaking, the changes in the melody – when the pitch goes up like a question and down like a statement – is pretty small and hard to follow. Similarly, the rhythm is very quick and in English it is quite varied. By exaggerating all of these aspects when we speak to babies we are helping them hear those differences[8].

If you listen closely to a parent using motherese or parentese, it almost sounds like a song. This is where singing to your baby comes in. Quite naturally we speak/sing to our babies and all we are doing is exaggerating speech and allowing our babies to hear the differences in sounds. So as parents we can all sing and to a point, the ability to sing in tune doesn't matter, but by singing to our babies we are giving them the opportunity to process the very complex set of sounds that make up speech[9]. What is most interesting to me is that babies who are not surrounded by high levels of parentese or song can experience a delay in their acquisition of speech[10], which can cause other developmental issues in their ability to express themselves and start managing their emotional responses.

Here is another amazing research discovery about singing and babies. Research has shown how a parent's singing, but particularly a mother's singing, can change the arousal level of their baby[11]. A common association might be singing a lullaby-type song – a slow, deep, soothing song – as a way of calming your little one down ready for sleep. One might call it 'the lullaby effect'.

What I find most interesting about the research is it has looked at the differences between the time it takes to calm a baby when they are being held and rocked; held and rocked and sung to; or when they are in their bed or crib and being sung to. Which one do you think saw the babies calm down more quickly and have deeper and better sleep? The one where they were *in their crib but being sung to*. Your voice is a very powerful tool.

Parents often say to me "my child is so musical, he/she walks around the house singing all day". I feel like an ogre when I want to answer that their child isn't exceptionally musical, they are just using singing, in part, to practise their speech. As their parent, your voice is their first and most important source of music that helps them learn how to first hear and then produce speech.

For that very reason, your voice will always be good enough for your child, because to them you are their favourite singer, their personal rockstar. Your voice is their window to the world (and they don't know what singing in tune sounds like anyway at the start of their life, so you sound great!).

Try your own experiments

Secret humming

Singing to anyone, even a baby, when you haven't done it for a long time can be rather confronting. That's okay. Singing is a learned skill, not a magical gift (researchers out there just go with me for a moment). If the last time you remember singing was in school, which might be (ahem) some time ago, take it slow and start by humming. Find a quiet place with your little one, or even on your own, and try humming your favourite tune. If it is important to you, do it when there is no one who can overhear you. Just listen to the qualities of your voice, maybe even imagine what colours might be in your voice, and try not to judge. Just observe. If you are singing to your baby, watch their face. Do they stop and watch you intently, do they squirm (remember babies have the attention span of a gnat), or do they respond with their own sounds? When you are ready, try using words. However, the words aren't so important, it is the emotion and variation you infuse into your humming/singing that your baby is most attracted to.

Listen out for parentese

Next time you hear your child's other parent or caregiver speaking to them, see if you can hear some parentese happening. Watch your little one's responses and think about what they are responding to. Often it is a combination of the speech/singing voice, the facial expressions and the familiarity with the person. I met a lovely four-month-old baby on the weekend and found myself making parentese kind of sounds. He looked at me quizzically, I think because my speech/song was new to him and he was processing the new combination of sounds that made up this new voice to him.

Get comfortable with your rockstar persona

By singing to your baby you are ultimately helping them develop the ability to learn how to speak. The way you sing to them can be a combination of your own musical tastes and the musical styles that your baby responds to. You might like death metal, but when you sing it your little one might not be so fond of it, so try the same song in the style of the Wiggles or a country singer. You might love Taylor Swift, but your baby seems to respond to an operatic version of one of her hits. What matters is that you are singing and enjoying music with your young one[12]. An added bonus is it can do great things for your own wellbeing. More about that in Chapter 7.

A little note about research

As I write this book, a lot of research is being conducted into the genetic predisposition for musical ability. In plain language, this research is trying to find out if we are born with musical ability. It is trying to answer the much bigger question of how much of human development is nature (what we are born with) or nurture (what we experience or learn). So far, not only in the area of musical ability, but in just about everything, they are looking at the idea that we are all born with slightly different predispositions for everything and that what we experience in life either enhances that predisposition or not.

As parents of little ones, I think we spend the first few years of their lives trying to answer this very question. Scientific research can explore this question in many different ways and it is important when reading articles supported by research that we understand that the research identifies probable trends and reveals important commonalities, but every child is a little different and every environment has its own unique elements.

Chapter 2

Getting in sync

How can singing help you get in sync with your child?

Even though my daughter is almost seven years old, I still wake regularly at three am. The reason I mention her age is I am pretty sure my body still thinks I have to get up for her three am feed. I am hoping (in vain, I think) that by the time she leaves home, my body might have figured out I don't need to wake up to breastfeed in the dead of night.

Three am turned out to be my favourite time during the first year of my daughter's life. Weird, I know, but there was something magical about it. It was just her and me, everything was quiet, and I couldn't throw a load of washing on or fold her never-ending pile of onesies. There was nothing for me to do but concentrate on her, and her on me. Most nights I would hum or sing to her, sometimes to keep myself awake and sometimes to distract myself from the sound of mice running around in our roof during the once in one-hundred-year plague we had that summer.

These were the times I felt closest to her and we seemed to intuitively understand each other. I once described it to a friend as the space between us, or the third space, where we knew and trusted one another, and I felt most confident that I could do this parenting thing and she could do this growing up thing. Not every night was great and magical but some were, and it astounded me how much the process of motherhood made me value the smaller moments when they came (like going to the toilet on your own – I mean really, kid!).

I didn't put much stock in this experience until just last year when I got to observe an experiment that blew my mind. I now think of all of those new parents out there singing to their children in moments of calm or desperation and every emotion in between, and I feel like I know something so incredible now that I just have to share it.

One day in Canada I saw a science experiment ...

I have had the great privilege of going on what I call road trips (it is rarely by road, mostly flights and loads of Ubers, but just imagine your favourite road trip song in your head). I have visited four countries, 15 labs, observed or undertaken 13 experiments and interviewed 93 researchers. That is a lot of time in windowless rooms with some really smart people. Thank goodness I made copious notes because it has all become a bit of a blur (add jetlag to that most of the time too). But one experiment shook me to my core; it was the best real-time example of how music and singing to our babies develops their brain.

Imagine a sound booth, like in a radio station. Inside is a lovely mother and her eight-month-old son. They are facing each other and are wired up with tiny pads on their fingers and feet. These pads measure galvanic skin response, or GSR, which is a really easy and effective way to measure emotional arousal through your skin; basically, it measures our sweat.

Changes in our sweat in the tiniest little ways are not under our conscious control and therefore it can help us understand our emotional responses and regulation. Outside the room there is a screen that shows the responses for mum's GSR and bub's GSR. The two super-talented researchers and I watch the screen with anticipation.

The task for mum is to sing *Twinkle, Twinkle Little Star* to her lovely son. She gets to sing it two different ways, one like a lullaby and one in a more playful way. On the outside of the booth we get to watch for any changes in their two lines on the screen. *Riveting stuff,* you may be thinking sarcastically.

But it is riveting. What happens is amazing. While mum and bub are in the booth, chatting, she is feeding him grapes, he is looking around, and the two lines on the screen look like an etch-a-sketch operated by two kittens – two lines going everywhere with no discernible pattern.

Then mum starts to sing. It doesn't matter which version of the song she sings, the same thing happens. Almost immediately when she starts to sing, the lines become pretty straight and they move in almost exactly the same way. They have synchronised and they stay synchronised for most of the song. Mum finishes singing and the lines go back to looking like an etch-a-sketch operated by kittens. I watched this happen multiple times and each time it was the same experience and gave me the same sense of wonder.

This is literally called synchronicity in the research. I was so lucky to spend an entire day with one of the pioneering researchers in this field, Dr Laura Cirelli, at Dr Sandra Trehub's lab in Canada. Synchronicity is her brain baby and she has done incredible work. Through this experiment that I described above, she has found a way to show through physiological measures, what so many parents experience as they sing and bond with their babies.

A previous, larger study found that singing to your baby helps create a bond and connection between mother, helps moderate both baby's and mother's emotional states and singing can communicate information between baby and mother[13].

This takes me back to some desperate times when I didn't know why my daughter was crying (I think she just liked the sound of her own voice), but I would sing to her: "You've got a dry nappy and a full belly, you've had a sleep and a play so you're happy, so why are you crying?" Now I look back on it and realise my singing might have helped me hold back my own tears that were probably just under the surface.

As this research has progressed Laura has found out even more about this phenomenon. When mum sang in a playful way, mum's excitement was higher and bub was paying more attention. When mum sang in a soothing lullaby way, both mum and bub's excitement went down as the song progressed. And here is the best bit: mum and bub were most in sync when mum was singing the lullaby[14].

When I was planning my most recent road trip I made a point of going to labs that specialise in working with infants. This was for a few reasons. One was I hadn't visited a lab that worked with infants and I wanted to know, as a new mother with a squirmy baby who was now a wriggly toddler, how they managed to get strange-looking EEG caps on their tiny heads, and get them to lie still inside fMRI machines (there is no trick, they fall asleep or watch a movie). Another reason was that I wanted to understand how babies processing sound and music was revealing the very first steps in human development, and how integral sound and music was to those first steps.

It turns out that babies prefer singing to speech[15] and babies pay attention for longer when mother is singing as opposed to speaking. Singing has been proven to heighten emotional communication[16] between mother and baby. Babies might have innate music-detectors[17] and they can use this skill to learn about music and all the other sounds around them. The amount of research in this area is huge and many other books are filled with the extraordinary work of researchers who work exclusively in this field.

From dipping my toe into this research and from having the privilege of talking with and witnessing many experiments with infants, I have come to understand that singing to our babies isn't just something nice to do or an added extra if you have "time". It serves very real, measurable and vital outcomes for our little one's development and it is the quickest, most powerful and, dare I say, cheapest way to connect with your bub.

Try your own experiments

The three am concert

Try singing to your little one when you have nothing else but time. Choose your favourite song at this moment in time; it could be Ed Sheeran or Maria Callas (maybe don't sing as loud as she did) and give it a go. Watch your little one's reaction. Do they stare at you; do they move or become very still; do they maintain eye contact with you; what happens to their breathing? Then, observe your own reactions. I was reminded recently that as parents our breathing tends to become shallower as we fling ourselves from one task to the next. Singing forces us to take deeper breaths, which is the first step in any meditation or mindfulness exercise.

Notice when you are in sync

I was often reminded by well-meaning people in my daughter's first few years to savour this time because it goes so quickly. Honestly, I couldn't wait for her next developmental step that allowed her to be more independent (I still remember the day she could hold her own bottle for a feed. I was no longer prisoner of the couch holding her bottle for her – I can still feel the thrill). But I became aware of those moments of synchronicity, and I switched on all my sensors to make a vivid memory of it.

I also described the feeling to my husband and through describing it out loud, I had a clearer idea what I was searching for in the times that were not so synchronous. Try being aware of synchronicity when it happens and if you don't want to describe it verbally to someone, try writing it down. Note what you were singing at the time, or which type of sounds brought you in sync. I found being in sync lasted for moments at a time, but they were powerful moments.

My husband had his own moment of synchronicity. I was not home (probably on a road trip) and our daughter was desperately ill with a vomiting disaster. He was using parentese to calm her and he remembers her looking up at him with great trust that he would be there for her as she felt so unwell. We usually just call it love and it is, but one aspect of love is getting in sync.

Chapter 3

Grooving to music

How do baby's ears teach their bodies to move?

I returned to full-time work when my daughter was seven months old. For her, going to day care each day worked out really well. She is an only child and honestly, my husband and I were just not enough for her. She is a social little being and loves being in a group of people, whether they are adults or children.

My mum, a primary and early childhood teacher for 40 years before she retired, volunteered to take my daughter to a music class once a week. I won't mention the name, but it was a well-known program based on solid early childhood research and well-developed teaching practices. I liked that my mum, and often my dad, got this special time with their granddaughter. They would take a picnic and sit under the big tree outside the centre after class and just enjoy each other.

The classes were what you would expect from a good music program: lots of singing, activities with small musical instruments, keeping the beat and moving different body parts in response to music. A lot of play and exploration and all those good things for growing brains.

Sometimes I got to go too, and it was fun to observe my body baby responding to the stuff that my brain baby was learning about. I distinctly remember going to one session when I was deep into the research on music and movement, and having this slightly split personality experience where I kept switching from proud parent to inquisitive researcher and back again. I have a favourite photo from that day and I can feel that conflict even now when I look at it.

One of the memories I have which used to make me laugh was the lack of recognition that my daughter, and other babies I observed, had for her limbs. They were like a surprise to her every time she saw them, like a goldfish going around in circles and seeing the fake dinosaur skull (I am referring to my daughter's fish tank) and feeling the same sense of surprise, "Ooh there's a dinosaur skull in here with me" (swim, swim, swim), "Ooh there's a dinosaur skull in here with me".

This was most noticeable when she was trying to clap her hands. For ages it seemed impossible to do; she would fling her hands towards each other and they would miss by a mile. Then she would stare at her hands with that "ooh, dinosaur skull" look as if to say "where did they come from?" Then she would try to clap again. Endlessly amusing for all involved, really.

I applied my rudimentary knowledge of the brain to this and thought that what I saw made sense. The right hand is operated by the left side of the brain and vice versa and the connective bit between the two hemispheres, the corpus callosum, or as one researcher called it, "the brain bridge", wasn't highly developed yet. So clapping her hands was tough because it required messages to travel across the brain pretty quickly. It is a normal process in a baby's brain development, but I had no idea that my daughter's ears were actually part of the equation and that there was this incredible timing puzzle she was trying to solve.

Ready for the science?

Stay with me, this is a bit of a mind bender: Babies use what they *hear* to teach their bodies how to *move*. Let me explain how cool this idea is.

Remember that our ears are information-gathering systems and they are always working? Well, with babies that means their brains are collecting information not just to label different things around them by the sound they make, such as the washing machine and the milk-making machine called Mum; they are also collecting information to connect parts of their brain.

The human brain is made up of structures (bits of the brain) and functions (how the brain works). I like to think of it as the structures being the buildings in a city and the functions being the roads in that city. Things can change in both aspects of the brain; the buildings can get refurbished or added to, and the roads can be widened or rerouted.

The system we primarily use to make our body move is called the motor system or cortex (cool brain word for part). The motor cortex is responsible for voluntary movements, but it isn't a law unto itself; it takes guidance from lots of other parts of the brain before it makes a move. For that guidance to get through, the pathways or connections need to be reliable and consistent.

Thinking about our building and road analogy, if we want to reliably get to the local shop we want an appropriately sized and maintained road that gets us there in about the same amount of time, every time. Connections between different parts of the brain are the same in a fully developed brain, but in a baby those connections are pretty unreliable because they haven't had much use yet.

Two of the connections that neuroscientists have been looking at are the auditory–motor (ears–body)[18] connection and the sensory–motor (ears–eyes–smell, etc.)[19] connection. Why have they been looking at it? Well, in the current field of research many neuroscientists are using music as a tool to understand how the brain develops and works. Through doing this, they are discovering how the human brain learns to talk to itself, to communicate information in weird and wonderful ways. In babies, the way the auditory cortex and the motor cortex learn to talk to each other is fascinating.

Think about your own reaction when you hear a piece of music. The sound goes into your ears. Then your various auditory processes start taking the music apart, comparing it to other music you have heard, listening to certain aspects of it, throwing it all back together again, telling your emotions if, on the whole, you like it, then sending a message to part of your body to respond.

If you are driving, this might be your head bobbing, or your index finger tapping the steering wheel. If you are sitting down, you might tap you hand on your leg or your foot on the floor. If you are doing the dishes you might give your hips a little wiggle (you know you do, don't be shy). That's your auditory cortex talking to your motor cortex.

Now stop wiggling and tapping, and think for a minute. How long is it between hearing the music and moving your body? Seconds? It might also be accompanied by a smile and an "oh yeah", but it all happens very quickly.

One of the key parts of this brain talking is musical beat. I often have to laugh in supermarkets where just-walking toddlers hear the background music and start to bounce to it. It is super cute, usually because they are smiling and by that time the parent has given up trying to do the shopping in anything resembling a short period of time. But this is what is happening in their brain.

Baby hears the music, baby likes the music, baby's brain processes the music and wants to move, baby's body tries to move to the beat, but the connections or pathways aren't very strong or wide yet so baby's dance looks like one of those blow-up figures outside a car dealership. Like I said, super cute!

The desire to move in time is what makes the auditory and motor cortices talk to each other. And music is the most powerful mechanism to facilitate that talking. Music immediately connects very closely with our emotional state[20]. This is why we use it to help calm ourselves down or get energised, and why music is pretty much part of every important event through our lives. The combination of using our ears to hear something, telling our body to do something and then feeling good about doing it, is the perfect combination[21] for learning.

This brain talking aspect of development is just the tip of the iceberg. The concept of timing within the human brain is very interesting because it is when there is a lack of timing that we start to see learning and behavioural problems occurring[22] [23].

Let's start with a simple one. If a child can keep a steady beat on a drum between the ages of three to four years, then it is likely they are going to exhibit normal or typical development in their reading at the age of five years. Okay, that was not *that* simple so let me explain.

The saying goes "timing is everything". Well, it actually is in this case. In a ground-breaking study[24] lead by Kali Carr it was found that the ability of a three or four-year-old pre-schooler to keep a steady beat on a drum was an indication that the right parts of their brain were connected in the right way so that the child was ready to start reading.

How does this happen? Well, this very simple exercise shows that the auditory–motor synchronisation is working properly, meaning that the motor output (the bodily movements) is synchronised with the auditory input (the sounds the child is hearing)[25]. If you think about the actions a young child has to do in order to read, it makes sense: first, they have to see the shape of the letters and words; second, they have to hear the sound that those letters make in their heads; third, they have to tell their mouths to move in the right way to make the right sound[26] [27].

This process became clearer to me when my daughter started to read. We received a suggestion sheet about what to do during her process of learning to read. One of the suggestions was to wait for longer than you think to allow your child to speak the word they are reading. For me, an avid talker who struggles with patience, this was a killer. But again, I went back to my body/brain baby and watched this process with an understanding that my daughter's brain was working on honing the timing between the visual, auditory and motor cortices. I would actually look at the top of her head and imagine pretty neurons firing around her brain (for some reason hers were purple; I'm not sure why), and that would help me wait for her to either figure out the word or ask for help.

This connection idea – the futuristic city inside my daughter's head with growing buildings, flying cars and purple-coloured roads – became even clearer for me when I asked a researcher about the connection between reading words and reading music.

Musical notation – all those dots and lines on a page that children learn when they are learning music – is also teaching a symbol-to-sound connection. The symbol on the page indicates a particular note (pitch) for a particular length of time (rhythm). A child needs to identify what the symbol means, hear the sound in their head, tell their motor cortex to move their fingers and body into a particular configuration and then add movement like a pull down on a violin bow or blowing air into a clarinet. This is why it is thought that learning music and learning how to read are complementary activities and many skilled researchers have followed this idea into early childhood classrooms[28] [29].

A friend and researcher I greatly respect said to me a bit offhandedly when I was right at the start of my PhD that I would only figure out the question I was trying to answer when I was three years into the six-year stretch it should take to finish my PhD part time.

This was devastating for me; I thought I had it all figured out (a bit like parenting – oh, how naïve I was). But damn her, she was right.

My investigations into music education and neuroscience were actually trying to answer a much deeper question for me. Did learning an instrument change my life? Because when I was younger I was not very good at reading.

If you want to hear this story from my own mouth, put this book down and go to my TEDx Talk on YouTube. Preparing to do a TEDxTalk was an extraordinary experience that helped me find this deeper question. If you are feeding bub right now and can't move, here it is in a nutshell.

My gorgeous mum, who is the star of this chapter, was not just a teacher, she was a remedial reading teacher. I was her first-born and through the first few years of my schooling I was struggling to read. Talk about some tension in the household (remembering this is my version of what happened, Mum may tell it very differently).

I remember coming up with lots of tricks to look like I was reading but my Year 1 teacher, Mrs Armitage, used to get me to come to her classroom every morning to "read". This translated into me staring at the book and trying to make sense of the pictures and the words I recognised. This continued for a few years and I will say my confidence and sense of self took a beating during this time, and I still regularly return to that little child within me who thinks she is a bit dumber than everyone else and can't learn very well. Sometimes, I think I did a PhD to prove to myself (and by extension the world) that I had some smarts.

I digress. At the age of nine there was a selective band program at the school and I was chosen to participate. We were collecting our instruments and when it was my turn I gave them my form, which indicated I was best suited to play the flute. The teacher looked around and said they had run out of flutes, so she had to give me a clarinet. Just as well she did because to this day I cannot get a nice sound out of a flute, but I took to the clarinet like a duck to water.

Now the choice of instrument may not have been important, but I think that learning how to read musical notation as part of the process was a transformative experience for me. Musical notation made sense to me; there weren't any special rules like "i before e except after c" (except for all those times the rule doesn't apply) and I finally had a system that reinforced my symbol-to-sound connections.

Six months later I remember my teacher saying "you don't need my help anymore, you can read on your own". No words can express how good I felt – about me, about my capacity to learn and my ability to change myself. I will never know if these two experiences were connected, or if one had a causal relationship to the other, but this is my story and I'm sticking with it.

Try your own experiments

Your whole world is your dance floor

Next time you start to do a little groovin' in the kitchen when a great song comes on the radio (or even the newest jingle on TV – I won't judge) take notice of how and when your body is responding to the music. At what point do you start bouncing around. For me, it is usually when the catchy chorus kicks in and I start singing. Next, think about the process your brain has just completed to get to that point where the music is expressed physically through your body. Are there certain songs or types of music that get your body groovin' more readily? How do you feel after the song has finished, when your cortisol levels have normalised and your brain and body are pulsing with endorphins and dopamine? Is this feeling something that you could use regularly and maybe more deliberately? How do you feel about making dinner or getting your bub into the bath after you have listened and moved to a piece of music that just does it for you? Get groovin', mums and dads!

Keeping a baby beat

If you have a toddler between the age of three to four years, can they follow you when you are keeping a beat on a drum, and can they keep that beat going after the music has stopped playing? If they can, great; there are some seriously healthy neural connections going on inside their head. If they can't, don't you dare panic; your child and every child is different. Think about what kinds of opportunities they currently have to practise those skills and build those neural connections, or what opportunities could you begin to make for them to learn how to keep a steady beat? I'm not talking keeping a beat for a whole song, which is something even adults struggle with. I mean keeping a steady beat for eight beats, then 16 beats and then even 32 beats. Some of the best music for these kinds of activities are nursery rhymes like *Ring a Ring o' Rosie* or dance or pop music with a really steady beat. Lullabies are not that useful in this situation, but keep them ready for other experiments.

Chapter 4

The building blocks of language

How are music and language connected?

One Christmas, something very strange happened. Our daughter was walking, well, tottering, and was about 15 months old. We were with my husband's family in their lounge room for present-opening time and the sheer spectacle of the mounds of coloured paper containing unknown surprises bought the biggest smile to her face. The present-opening mania was about to begin, and her grandfather picked up the first present and read the label. "This one is for Oma," he said (our daughter has a truly multicultural set of grandparents: Oma, Grandpa, Yiayia and Grandad). Suddenly our daughter tottered over to Grandpa, took the present, tottered over to Oma and gave her the present. We were all stunned. She didn't have a great deal of language yet and had never used anyone's name besides Dada, which she didn't even seem to relate to her father.

So we tried again. Grandpa picked up another present and said the name on the tag. Our daughter dutifully tottered over, took the present, delivered it to the correct person and we all clapped when she got it right. This happened five more times and each time the present went to the correct person, with the funniest moment when Grandpa said our daughter's name and she looked around for the person and then realised it was her. She sat straight down and opened the present with gusto.

This experience got me thinking very deeply about how she understood language at this age. It was one of my "duh!" moments (picture Homer Simpson in your head – just add a facepalm). I realised I had thought she didn't understand language because she couldn't *speak* it yet. But she could understand language at a very deep level, it was just that her brain had not yet reached that development level where the sounds she heard could be replicated in her own voice. Any parent with a child in a child under 6 years old will know the process of articulate speech takes years and is constantly being refined to greater levels of clarity and content.

As my daughter travelled through the process of acquiring language I kept in mind that she was hearing language as if it were music. Music has many individual concepts or parts, but the most basic are melody and rhythm. Language has the same concepts or parts at its core[30]. Language sounds go subtly up and down as we speak to indicate implicit meaning and the length of sounds are the building blocks of words, sentences[31] and syntax.

This theory became real to me when my daughter started babbling. I often use this example when explaining this theory: A toddler speaks an entire sentence to a stranger and it makes no sense to the stranger, so the stranger looks to the parent. The parent then "interprets" the sentence for the stranger because they can understand their own child's melody and rhythm.

The babbling stage is a vital step towards becoming fluent in any language. What the toddler is missing as they babble are the gaps between the words (rhythm) and the subtle and appropriate inflections (melody). These will come with time, practice and a large number of varied experiences with language. In essence, lots of language inputs.

Now let's talk about the science...

Language inputs are basically lots of opportunities to hear the different sounds of language. Professor Nina Kraus, an eminent auditory researcher at Northwestern University in Illinois, USA, described the process to me in these 10 steps:

1. A baby hears a sound environment as one sound to start with, not as a lot of different sounds that combine to make a sound environment.
2. A baby's auditory system starts dissecting each sound environment into many different sounds. This takes a long time as a baby needs to be able to identify the direction the sound is coming from, the object or person that made the sound, whether the sound matches another sound they heard previously, and what might be the meaning of that sound, e.g. danger, safety or "my toy broke".
3. One of the most important sounds to identify in a baby's sound environment is speech as a separate sound from all the other sounds or noises. In the research this is called hearing speech-in-noise[32].

Once a baby can separate speech from all the other noise they start to try to mimic those sounds with their own voices.

4. Once a baby can identify speech from all the other noises they start to dissect speech itself into its parts.

5. The first sounds they pick out are vowels, because they are the most repeated sounds in the English language and they are actually the easiest sounds to produce. As a researcher explained it to me, they don't require fine motor skills; we just open our mouths, vibrate our vocal chords and the vowel sound comes out. This may be why we hear lots of *ah* and *ee* sounds from babies (there is one in the café where I am sitting right now who is certainly practising his *ah* and *ee* sounds very loudly).

6. The second type of sounds a baby and then toddler starts to dissect are consonants. This is much harder as babies struggle to hear the differences between them. For example *b* and *d* are similar sounds and hearing the difference is very hard[33]. They also don't occur as frequently as vowels so there are less language inputs for a baby to work with.

7. The third step is hearing when the language sounds change between the vowels and the consonants. We wouldn't know it, but there are tiny gaps between these changes that are called transitions. Babies need to hear when the sounds change in order to go from single sounds to words and phrases, and finally to sentences.

8. During this entire time babies are practising their phonological representation. This is a fancy phrase researchers use for producing the sound

through your voice that you hear in your head. Put another way, their ears have heard their name very often and they are trying to produce that sound themselves. Babies and toddlers are constantly repeating sounds as a way to practice synchronising the sounds their brains are making with the sounds their voice is making. This is why babies and toddlers can get fixated by a particular sound and say it incessantly for a number of days. They are practising producing the same sound out loud that they hear in their head.

9. At the same time, toddlers are learning the rhythm and melody of language[34]. In the research the melody part is called prosody, which is the patterns of stress and intonation in our language. I think of it as the information underneath the words, like the way we know if someone is genuinely feeling good or possibly troubled by something just by the way they say "I'm okay".

10. Next a baby starts to hear something that isn't actually there: the silences and tiny breaks between the words. Researchers call the package of sounds that we hear "the envelope". This envelope is basically made up of three parts: the attack of the sound at the start, the sustained sound in the middle, and the decay of the sound as it fades away. Imagine if you got to strike a really big bell. There is the bang at the start, the sound as the bell vibrates, and then it starts to soften. Once a baby has identified the envelope they can hear the tiny silences in the middle, which in music are called rests. When babies, now toddlers, have started to hear these gaps, those babbling sentences start

to make sense. This is when toddlers can start to communicate their thoughts, intentions and feelings. Remember, at this point their processing of prosody[35] – the melody underneath their words – is also developing, so sometimes you can hear your little one saying "I'm happy" with a mismatched angry or sad inflection.

The next phase is practise, practise, practise. By this time they are toddlers and I have noticed they can be anything from little chatterboxes or quite reserved with their speech. I often used to watch this magical time in my daughter's day care group when some children were more confident with language than others, but the level of language didn't seem to matter; they continued to communicate through their gestures, sounds and facial expressions. Some of the toddlers seemed to have no off-switch and would be practising their language out loud. Others were less verbal but when they did speak, their enunciation and sentence structure was very good, as if they had been practising internally to come out with a fully formed and correct piece of language.

Research has shown that the more varied language a baby or toddler is exposed to, and encouraged to engage with, the quicker they will acquire language. Furthermore, with consistent role modelling and correction they will continue to develop well into pre-school or primary school.

You might think we have moved away from music and into the world of language. But if you keep in mind that your little one is hearing the song/music-like qualities in language then this process is full of musical elements. My daughter and I used to have prosody conversations. These are a little hard to explain in writing and much easier to demonstrate. Let me give it a try.

A prosody conversation is like watching the Swedish Chef from *The Muppet Show* or observing a conversation between two people who speak another language to your own. My daughter and I used made-up sounds, inflections and lots of facial expressions and gestures to have a conversation. We didn't have a topic or purpose, we were just responding to each other's previous phrase. Afterwards, my daughter would make up elaborate stories that went along with the emotional content of our prosody conversation. An unexpected outcome of these conversations is that my daughter started adding in her own sentences to a conversation at family dinner. It didn't make sense to us, but it showed she could hear the intent of each part of the conversation and add in her own thoughts.

As a parent you may have had your own prosody conversations with your baby but next time you have one, think about all the information your baby is getting from both your speech and from interacting with you by using speech.

If we continue to think of language as a combination of melody and rhythm, teaching young children how to subtly change their language can become a game of music. I used to enjoy running experiments with my daughter. For example, one day my daughter said "Get my bag, Mum" in a demanding tone. I instinctively wanted to reply "Get it yourself", but I stopped for a moment to breathe. Then I responded like this:

Me: "Can we stop for a moment? I wasn't happy with your tone there. Can you tell me why?"

Daughter: "No." (a look of bewilderment on her face)

Me: "I found your tone very demanding and we don't speak to each other like that in our family. Firstly, is there a better way to phrase the same words?"

Daughter: "Get my bag, Mum, please?"

Me: "I like the please. How about also adding 'Could you get my bag please, Mum?'"

Daughter: "Could you get my bag pleeeeease, Mum?" (the please over-exaggerated and *way* too long)

Me: "Not bad. Now could we make the melody sound more like you are asking me for a favour? Does this sound like I am asking you to do something nice for me?" (I demonstrate a slightly over-exaggerated version of the phrase)

Daughter: "Could you get my bag please, Mum? Could you get my bag please, Mum? Could you get my bag please, Mum?" (emphasising different words and using different inflections)

By this time, my daughter and I are in the car and halfway to school, and we are *still* playing around with the phrase. We go back and forth trying out different versions, the sillier the better, and ultimately decide on the one that is the best for the purpose. This also leads to a conversation about the purpose of language, and the different ways to share information, to build relationships and to respect each other.

At the time, I was testing out research I had been reading about how day-old babies had highly active music-processing networks and that they were hearing their mother's voices as music[36]. I had also been reading about the delay in language acquisition of children growing up in disadvantage because they heard 30 million fewer words than children not living in disadvantage before the age of five[37]. Less language inputs means less language information for the brain to work with[38].

I was once asked by a parent who had observed one of these conversations between my daughter and me, where I found the time to "correct" her language. I pondered this question for a long time and it got me thinking about my role in her language learning. I came to the conclusion that I was giving my daughter language *options* rather than correction, allowing her to understand both her choice of words and listen to the messages she was conveying with her language melodies[39]. We did this process quite often during her terrible twos and threes (I think the threes might have been worse than the twos) and I have been surprised how focusing on her language choices at this time has paid dividends tenfold in the years since.

More recently as my daughter started school, I started hearing phrases come out of her mouth that sounded like a much older person. To my shock and horror, I realised she was sounding like my husband

and me. Again, this got me thinking about the language inputs she was soaking up like a sponge, and that we were a significant source of those inputs. The soundtrack of the way we spoke at home, both to her and to each other, the way we spoke in the car on speakerphone, and particularly during periods of stress or tension, were all feeding into the music of her language. It made me not only monitor the content of what I was saying, but the melody and rhythm of it as well.

Like all parents, we can't maintain our respectful, calm, positive mum and dad personas every minute of the day, but now when our voice has an edge to it or we are nervous or concerned, we have a vocabulary for talking about language that helps our daughter continue to examine her own spoken language.

Try your own experiments

Keep a language log

Thinking about language as music is a pretty mind-bending idea but you can use your little one as a source of data or information. Try to figure out which stage of language development your baby or toddler might be in and listen to the sounds they make. Are there any repeated sounds; is their babble in a repeatable rhythm or do their language melodies tend to end going up (a question) or going down (a statement)? Keep a log for a day, week or month and see if you can see changes. A log doesn't have to be words either; it can be lines that follow the melodies or frequency lists where you tick how often they make specific sounds. You don't need to keep it for long – just until you start hearing the music in their language.

Have a prosody conversation

Put your best Swedish Chef hat on and have a conversation with your bub using only sounds. Freeing yourself up from words and language often allows you to focus on the musical parts of language.

Rephrase the phrase

Try modelling different ways of delivering a simple instruction or request and see if your toddler can mimic you. Be warned this might not be met with the greatest enthusiasm to start with, but keep trying and see how they respond. Toddlers have a hair trigger and can explode at any time, so pick your moment and be patient.

Recognise warning tones

Often, siblings will have a tone that they use to aggravate their brother or sister. As parents you know what it sounds like – you are listening for it all the time – so you can launch a pre-emptive strike to defuse the conflict. Try helping each child be aware of that tone and to have alternate language melodies to use in those situations.

A little note about research

We often find out about typical brain development by studying *atypical* brain development. In the field of language development in children, this means you will see research studies about language development in children with autism, acquired brain injuries or genetic disorders. It feels a bit counter-intuitive, but by studying children as they develop in an atypical way it helps them to understand more about what is typical development. So don't be surprised when you see a journal paper that includes one of these developmental conditions; it is actually the scientific method hard at work, helping us understand the nature of brain development in children.

Chapter 5

Raising a helpful child
What does music have to do with my child being helpful?

Before my trip to Canada in 2017, if you had asked me to explain how music helped raise a helpful child I would have said "huh?" Those two ideas don't seem to be related at all and until I saw the experiment in action I would never have understood.

Let me take you back to that lab in Canada from Chapter 2 and the brilliant Dr Laura Cirelli. One of the other experiments I got to observe was studying a phenomenon that Laura has done pioneering work in – it is the connection between moving together and something called prosocial behaviour, which is when we voluntarily do something that is intended to help another person. If you are a parent of a toddler or a young one in the early years of school (actually, right through the teenage years), helping your child to understand when and how to do things for others seems like an unending task. So you will just love this story.

I'll describe the experiment I observed first and then talk about what I learned from Laura about this unlikely connection.

Infant labs don't look like labs, they are like playrooms with all the wires and equipment cleverly hidden behind screens and furniture. This is a good opportunity to explain something about psychological research.

When scientists do an experiment they have something called conditions, and there might be between two and four conditions in any experiment. A condition is basically one version of the activity – and often there are several – so that the researcher can compare the responses as a group. In medical research you might hear the word "placebo" used, which is a way of comparing those who got the experimental drug, to those who got a sugar pill instead. Research studies are designed like this because it helps to remove the issue of people reporting they feel better because they think they are getting a new wonder drug.

Anyway, a mother and her lovely 14-month-old daughter – let's call her Ruby – came into the lab in Toronto. Ruby was randomly assigned the control condition. Now, Laura had done this experiment with lots of different conditions with other children, which included bouncing in time with them. Now, imagine the bub facing forward, strapped to her mother's front in a carry harness. Laura put on some music and in one condition Laura bounced in time (synchronous movement) with mother and child and in the other she bounced out of time (asynchronous movement) with mother and child[40]. In another experiment, Laura sang a song, read a book or just sat near the child. Remember, the child had never met Laura before so she was a stranger to them, albeit a very nice one.

After Laura had either moved, sung, read or sat with the child, she did a couple of activities like hanging up clothes and drawing a picture. In both activities, she dropped the peg or pen and then reached for the item, all the time saying things like "oh-oh" or "oh-no". Laura did these activities several times, using her body language and eye contact differently to see if different types of attention techniques made any difference.

What Laura was searching for was the conditions in which Ruby was more willing to exhibit prosocial behaviour, to help out a grown-up stranger by picking up the peg or pen.

As she was assigned the control condition, it meant Laura didn't interact with her very much before she started the activities. What happened next was textbook. Every time Laura dropped a peg or a pen, Ruby just looked at her, looked at the peg or pen, looked at Laura and did absolutely nothing. I commend her mum for sitting close by and being able to keep her body still and mouth closed, because as parents we would jump in to help our little one to understand what the appropriate response was to such a situation.

This showed that at this age, helping behaviours are part of their behaviour, but not a regular or common part just yet. This why the idea that doing something before a child is put into a position where they have to make a decision to help the researcher out is so interesting.

Here comes the science ...

When I talked to Laura after the experiment, she said Ruby was a model research participant. She didn't help, not even a flicker of assistance even once during the 30-minute experiment. You might think, well of course she didn't, she's a toddler. This is where Laura's research is so brilliant! Across her many experiments she has found that toddlers are far more likely to be helpful when the researcher moves in time, bouncing to the beat with them, or when she sings a song that they know to them. And I am talking A LOT more likely. Something amazing happens when a stranger engages with a toddler by sharing music together.

There is a pretty big leap between moving or singing together and taking action to help another person. Why would sharing music make a difference? Laura and I talked a lot about this connection and while her research is ongoing, and scientists are loathe to come to definitive conclusions, she thinks it might be something to do with encouraging trust, and through trust comes empathy for another person, which in turn leads to taking action to help that person.

At the moment, Laura's research is showing that the toddlers are more helpful to a person they are moving and singing with. It doesn't necessarily mean that the toddlers are helpful individuals all the time[41]. However, this idea has been looked at by other researchers who have found that music-making in four-year-olds also promotes prosocial behaviours[42]. So that musicplay program my daughter went to with my mum (back in Chapter 3) might have had more impact than I knew.

Let me take you back to the village environment, when it truly did take a village to raise a child. Night-time activities often included songs and dance around the communal fire in which children would learn the history, stories and culture of their extended village family. These activities may well have been vehicles to engender a sense of belonging and trust (although right now I am aware I may be stepping on some sociologists' toes). But for me the idea is interesting. Human beings have had music for far longer than we have had our complex languages, so there may be far older and deeper ways of communicating and learning who to trust and care for.

I also wonder about the ways we continue to move and sing together as grown-ups. A very dear friend has just returned from the Burning Man festival in the USA. It is an incredible event where a city is temporarily created out of nothing more than what the attendees bring with them to the middle of an inhospitable desert. As part of the festivities, again created by people who are strangers to each other until they come to Burning Man, are dance parties and choir performances, which may access the same mechanism of moving and singing together, to create trust and empathy and a willingness to look after one another in an extreme environment.

I watch parents with their little ones and they naturally start to sway. I did it myself when my daughter was young and even now when I have the opportunity to hold a baby, I can't seem to stop the instinctive rhythmic movement from side to side. It actually feels odd not to move when we are singing a song or lullaby to our baby[43], which makes me wonder if the combination of singing and swaying with our babies is a behaviour that is buried very deep within us to encourage the trust that any family, extended or small, needs to function.

How does this relate to singing? A song is not really a song without a beat and very often we naturally find ourselves moving in time to a song we are singing to our little ones[44]. What we might not have understood until now is the impact it could have on our children in a seemingly disconnected idea of teaching our children when and how to help others. If we encourage empathy as early as we can, just think of the amazing teenagers and adults we are raising. And maybe my daughter will pick up her clothes because she knows how much it helps me!

Try your own experiments

It's all about the timing

Try your own prosocial behaviour experiment. Move in time with some music with your toddler, sing a very interactive song with them or clap along to a song together. Immediately after you finish the musical activity, experiment with your own helping activity. Maybe you go directly to unload the washing machine, take a few handfuls out and then drop some of the clothes on the floor. Reach down for them and make a sound like "o-oh" but don't pick them up, look to your little one and see if they understand your dilemma and move to help. It might take a few repetitions of "o-oh", but just see if he or she comprehends the problem and takes some type of action to help. It might not be the help that you wanted, but the recognition of the problem and the ability to help is what we are looking for. Once that happens, we as parents can build on that sense of empathy that is so hard for children to learn.

Become the trusted stranger

Try the same experiment with a toddler you have only just met. Best to check with their parent or grandparent first and explain what you have read about in this chapter (maybe even share a copy of this book with them!).

A little note about research

Where research comes from is important. What do I mean by that? Well, the field that any research study stems from is important to know when looking at what they discover. In this book, I am taking about both neuroscientists and psychologists, who are wildly different types of scientists and come from very different viewpoints. To make it even more confusing there are scientists who cross these fields, like cognitive neuroscientists, and studies that use both neuroscientific and psychological tests to answer their questions.

The reason I mention this is that neuroscientists tend to come from the point of view that what they see in brain activity translates into what we see someone do. Psychologists tend to believe there is a filter (actually, many) in between how the brain functions and how a person behaves, and therefore behaviour is what they study. To add to this debate neuroscience is a fairly new science and it is still working out what it all means, whereas psychology is a very well-developed science.

Consequently, as one psychologist in Germany explained it to me – neuroscientists are arguing about the method (the way they find things out) and the psychologists are arguing about the theory (the basis from which they understand what they know). These are two totally different things so when you read an article based on research, take note of the field the researcher comes from.

I had no idea about the intellectual war that was raging between these two fields until I met with, and had every idea I had ever held true challenged by, Professor Glenn Schellenberg in Canada (it's all happening in Canada). If you want to read more about this, check out his excellent and confronting paper listed in the endnotes[45].

Chapter 6

Brain food

How does music make my baby's brain grow?

It's a catchy title isn't it, food for the brain? It strikes me as the type of title I might see in the parenting aisle at my local bookstore. It's funny; as I try to decide on an anecdote to start this chapter, I keep thinking how cheesy the title is, but it also encapsulates what I have come to understand is a vital vitamin for a growing baby's brain.

Vitamin M for Music. Let's call it that. Although I think it might be equally appropriate to call it Vitamin S for Sound.

My daughter was singing this morning in her usual fashion while she was getting ready for school. Her song today was a mixture of non-descript melodies, just "la-la-la", punctuated by sudden and very loud words like "my BIRTHDAY is in two days, two days, two D-D-DAAAAYYYYYSSSSSSSSSS" (picture Bette Milder rocking out a massive note at the end of her show at the Hollywood Bowl … Wow, two days? I better get this book finished!). As I came to the end of my first draft of this book and listened to her sing, it struck me how much I have learned from her and how much Vitamin Music has been part of her life because of my research.

What have I learned? I'm glad you asked. I have learned that my daughter's sound environment is one of the most important things I have been able to provide to her in almost seven years. It has not just been about providing sounds to her, it has been about learning from how she has responded to sound and taking steps to expose her to sounds and sound experiences that have made it possible for her brain to grow and thrive.

There is a great book by Liisa Henriksson-Macaulay called *The Music Miracle*[46], which does a fantastic job of breaking much of this research up into smaller chunks. She describes what music and music learning does for a baby's brain as "building highways where dirt tracks would have been".

Babies absorb enormous amounts of information right from the beginning of their lives. Their brains spend a lot of time figuring out what to do with that information, where to store it, if it matches or not with information they have had before, if it has meaning for them yet, or if it is something they think they should hang on to for later. Every time information travels along a path, it changes the path, maybe the direction, the width of the path or the surface of the path (go with me neuroscientists, I know I am stretching the analogy).

How does Vitamin Music help that path-making? Well, imagine five removalist trucks arrive simultaneously at your new home, each with a logo saying "**Eyes** Incorporated", "**Ears** Are Us" or "A **Touch** of Class Removals"; that's three of your five senses. The Ears truck is the biggest, as it has the biggest amount of stuff to move in, and the guys on this truck don't listen to instructions; they just plough into your house and put stuff anywhere.

Now, anyone who has moved house will know there are two approaches: unpack stuff close to where it should be, and you can sort it out later (takes a day to unpack), or go through each box methodically and think about the best place to put it the first time (takes a week to unpack). My tendency for the first approach inevitably means I don't end up moving things into a more appropriate spot later on and the house remains just that little bit dysfunctional. If I took the time at the start to unpack in a considered way, life in the house would be a lot better right from the start.

Taking the time at the start of your little one's life to understand how they use sound to grow their brain will benefit them in the long run. If the pathways they develop for processing sound at the beginning of their lives are like well-maintained highways, learning language, both spoken and then written, is a much easier journey. If your baby's connection with you and with other members of their village is consistent, trusting and joyful, then the path to managing their emotional states and being considerate and empathic towards others is less bumpy. If the pathways between the different buildings in your baby's brain, the different senses and associated networks are healthy and responsive, then your baby is well prepared to thrive when they reach school and start to develop into an independent learner.

I am often asked these two questions: "Which lullabies 'work'?" and, "Is classical music better for my child's development?" If music is our Vitamin M for the brain, then these would be my answers.

Which lullabies "work"?

The prickly researcher in me would counter this question with "what do you define as 'work'?" And it is a reasonable question; we traditionally use lullabies to help our babies go to sleep, so does "work" mean they go to sleep or stay asleep; does it refer to the quality of their sleep or the mood they wake up in after their sleep? In the end, lullabies are a certain kind of song used to induce a certain kind of emotional state. This is usually a calm and relaxed state that sometimes promotes sleep. The musical characteristics of a lullaby are usually a slower song, sung in a soft voice in a lower part of your vocal range, but the content could be anything. Think about some of the popular lullabies like *Rock-a-Bye Baby* and *Hush Little Baby*. Think about the words: babies falling out of trees and broken mirrors, fallen horses and mockingbirds that won't sing ... the content of a lullaby doesn't matter to a baby, it is the music you bring to the song. As I have said, you could be singing the Tattslotto numbers or the words from a Metallica or Justin Bieber song. It wouldn't matter to your little one. However, the person it *does* matter to is you, and for you to sing in a comfortable and confident way you need to *like* what you are singing.

Is classical music better for my child's development?

I like to answer this question by saying that music is just sound; it is what we do with those sounds when they enter our ears and our brains that makes it music. Daniel Levitin, of *This is your Brain on Music* fame, describes them as ones and zeroes[47]. Our brains go through a highly complex series of processes to make sense and meaning out of the sounds that we call music[48]. To me, what is different about styles of music is their level of complexity and therefore the level of processing (and experience) required to make meaning out of them.

Music has the same ingredients wherever you go. These are the ingredients that your child will probably learn about in their music class in school, and roughly speaking they are rhythm (fast and slow notes), pitch (which includes melody and harmony), tempo (speed of the music), dynamics (volume of the music), tone colour (the source and characteristics of the sound) and expressive techniques (not what you think – these are the musical details). Music is made up of different choices and a combination of those ingredients. It is rather like cooking. There are a thousand ways to cook chicken; the variation comes with how you cook it and what you put with it.

Let's start with a good old pop song. A pop song isn't very high on the complexity scale and this is why. Pop songs are usually three minutes long, there's a lot of repetition in the song, there's usually structure that is easy to anticipate with verses and a chorus (and a guitar hero solo if it came from the 80s) and they have a catchy tune that we can remember. The instrumentation is usually pretty standard with a rhythm part (drumkit), bass part (electronic or guitar), harmony part (piano or guitar) and a melody part (a singer or two). A pop song makes sense quickly, is easy to remember, uses a format we know and doesn't tax our brains too much to process. Please note that nowhere in this description have I said any of this makes it *bad* music, it's just like quickly digestible fast food. Just the thing when you need it.

Now, let's jump to the other end of the complexity scale: a classical music symphony (music people out there, I am using the generic term for music with a symphony orchestra but please let it slide). A symphony can last for 60 minutes, contain four contrasting movements, contain very little repetition or if it does, the theme might be played at the start and then you get to hear it 45 minutes later (or if it's Wagner, three days later), and probably in a different key and played by a different instrument. The variety of instrumentation is immense, with maybe 20 different types of instruments, but they can also be played in different combinations, which exponentially increases the number of different tone colours your brain has to process. Again this is not *good* music, it is just more complex and you might get a slightly numb backside listening to it, but it is rather like a degustation. A meal that dazzles the senses and makes your tastebuds (and digestive system) work much harder.

Why compare the two? Because we have all these different types of music that we use and enjoy for different reasons at different times. We don't eat fast food every day and we don't go out for degustation every night. Our brains like and need variety.

Our ears like and need variety too, but this need for complexity can have a transfer effect on other functions within the brain. If we only ever experience simple pop-style music, then those brain pathways are very specific, narrow and specialised. Interestingly, it seems that this narrowness can have an impact on other narrow thinking, like valuing of difference, seeking out new challenges and thinking creatively[49]. But we can't just ask our children, or ourselves, to jump to processing and making meaning from a classical symphony when we might have only ever listened to pop songs.

If we think of music as food, we start with the simple foods like mushed apple and pumpkin and then we slowly introduce and come to enjoy more complex foods. But it takes years to develop our auditory-processing skills around music. It can be helped by listening to more music, seeking out podcasts about music and even learning to play an instrument as an adult (I took up cello this year, and that's a whole other book of learnings: stay tuned).

Try your own experiments

Choose a different station

We usually have our car radio tuned to our favourite station. Next time you get in the car, choose one that is complete different. Listen to the music and monitor how you feel, what you think and how many new sounds or musical ideas you hear. Remember, music is very closely connected to our emotional state, so listening to something different might feel uncomfortable. But if you remember it is about widening your own brain pathways, you might be more willing to live with a little discomfort for a short time.

Sometimes I invite my daughter to pick the music in the car. When this started it was a great language development tool because I would ask her "can you describe the music you would like to hear?" At the start she would simply say "fast", "big", "ballet", but she got better at it and now I get "I feel tired from school, can

I have some relaxing music without anyone singing please?"

Sing the ingredients for spaghetti sauce

I challenge you to pick the most outrageous words to sing to your baby in a lullaby style. Did they pick up the difference? Did you feel better after you had a little sing?

A little note about research

Let me take a moment to talk about transferability and how we interpret findings from research studies in general. It is important to keep in mind that at this time it is extremely difficult to measure how learning a musical instrument might transfer across to a seemingly unrelated activity such as solving maths questions. There are so many things that can influence a child's development such as genetic factors, individual personality and environmental influences, that designing an experiment that proves unequivocally that any one activity develops every child the same way is impossible.

What we can find through the scientific method are commonalities or possibilities. If you have ever wondered how much you can trust the findings of a study, particularly when you read the words "research says..." or "a new study has found...", I suggest you take a look at Daniel Levitin's book *A Field Guide to Lies and Statistics*[50], in which he explains in a very understandable way how to decide if and how much you can trust the research findings you hear or read about.

Chapter 7

Singing the blues away
Singing as medicine?

In previous chapters I started with an anecdote about something I observed in either my daughter's or other children's development. This chapter is about me.

Big breath in ... and out.

I'm sitting in another café; not one of my regular ones but one that's full of café noises nonetheless (perhaps if I had a recording of café sounds I could actually write at home instead of procrastinating by tidying up the kitchen?). I have been sitting here biting my lip and staring into space, trying to think of an anecdote to begin this chapter. Then it comes to me – not the beginning, but an answer. This little book is a bit like my PhD; I have only figured out the real reason I am writing it and the question I am trying to answer, when I'm most of the way through it.

The question is, what happened to me over the last seven years? That isn't meant to sound negative; actually, I am doing a little prosody exercise in my head and I can ask that question in at least four different ways with four very different answers. Let me explain a little more about my "Seven Years as a Parent" (when

I sometimes felt like I was living in a far-off foreign land like Tibet) and maybe the meaning of the question will become clear.

I didn't like being pregnant ... AT ALL! This seemed like an ungrateful reaction since we didn't fall pregnant just like that; we had to get help to make it happen. So why was it when we had worked hard to get to the point of expecting a baby that I was not having a good time? I have to laugh at this now because nowhere in the product description did it say "pregnancy = happy feelings!"

Not everyone finds pregnancy hard. A friend of mine who was pregnant not long before me with her first child said she felt like a superhero; like she could do anything. Everyone is different, and everyone's journey is unique (I sound like a greeting card). I had started my PhD before I was pregnant and as the road to pregnancy was not the easiest, and by no means a certain one, I felt it important to have a baby of my own – my brain baby. At least I had more control over what happened with a brain baby.

Once our daughter came into the world, I struggled to balance the additional role I now had with the very full life I had before I was pregnant. I freely admit I made the choice to go back to work full time, and that it was the right decision for me and, I believe, for my daughter. Everyone is different; everyone's choices are unique (now I sound like a self-help book – I'm covering all the bases). I was as committed to my brain baby as I was to my body baby but as I said in the introduction, they couldn't coexist for very long so I became super-efficient about everything.

I have watched many other mothers and fathers do exactly the same thing in their own way, after they take on the role of parent. Makers' fairs all around the world are filled with new parents who have started their own brain babies in the form of businesses when their little ones have been very young. Completing a PhD and starting a business isn't that different; they both involve lots of planning, false starts, pilot projects and a big dose of effective project management. I applaud all those parents out there for pursuing their own brain babies when they have body babies who can demand so much of their time and energy.

But it is not all sunshine and rainbows and by answering my "what happened?" question I am trying to put a full stop on my experience over the last seven years. I am trying to encapsulate the unique opportunity I had in having a body and brain baby at the same time and to acknowledge all that it gave me and all that it cost me. The cost was high, and the benefits were also high. But while I was in the middle of it, it just seemed like my own little form of madness.

You might be wondering where the science is going to come into this story. Never fear … here it is. Singing connects us to ourselves when the world around us is our own little form of madness.

The science of singing

As I mentioned, I learned the clarinet – and a lot of the research into the impact of music learning has been done around that very activity: learning a musical instrument. When I present to teachers and parents, without fail the second or third question is always "what about the impact of singing?" The answer is, singing connects very directly and clearly to our sense of wellbeing.

This is the area where learning music and health cross over beautifully and before there was music education there was music *experience*. It is often quoted that every culture has its own form of music and that music is unique to humans[51]. So this begs the question: as human beings, did we make music for enjoyment or did our evolutionary development create music as a tool for brain development?

This is a very tricky concept and I won't even attempt to enter into this field in this book. I'll leave that to the eminent scholars and thinkers who already write in this area (read their stuff, it's really good!). But I will ask you to sit with this question for a while: Did we make music, or did music make us?

There are some fascinating scholarly writings on this very question[52] [53] [54] [55]. One of the many interviews I have done in the last two years touched on this question and one perspective intrigued me. Professor Laurel Trainor leads the Music and the Mind lab at McMaster University in Canada. When I interviewed her, I was conscious that I felt both intensely calm and intellectually turned on (there, I've said it) at the same time.

We spoke about her idea that music could have different roles to play in our lives at different times. When we are babies and toddlers, it may help us to learn to communicate through language and also develop our auditory system to detect danger and thus survive (or not). Later in life, it could be used for emotional self-regulation and health. Essentially, she is proposing the idea that there is not one answer for why we have music, but I have tried to encapsulate an incredibly complex idea in to a few sentences. Look up

Professor Trainor's work and the work around this idea if you want to know more[56].

I mention her work because this idea that we can use music, specifically singing, in different ways throughout our lives has stuck with me. Singing has a direct link to our emotions and after all the language learning, social cohesion and survival purposes that it serves, it continues to improve how we feel. In numerous large studies into choirs, the participants' levels of wellbeing improved in a number of different ways[57 58 59].

Conversely, mothers and fathers who experience post-natal depression are less likely to engage with their babies through song[60]. Singing has been found to promote sleep for newborns and improve outcomes for premature babies, including babies who require intensive care at the beginning of their lives[61]. Singing calms babies down faster when they are distressed and one study found that play songs, like *Insy Winsy Spider*, were more effective than lullabies at reducing arousal in babies[62]. All this research shows that we use music and singing for many reasons in the first few years of our little one's life – to create a bond, to induce trust, as a signal of familiarity and safety, to reduce distress and moderate the emotional state of both parent and baby.

Looking after my daughter in her first six months saw me more housebound than I had ever been before. I remember spending 45 minutes trying to get her ready for a walk around the block in her pram (you know the drill – all packed and ready to go when suddenly she needed a nappy change, then she threw up enough so she needed a new top, then she needed another nappy change, then she grizzled like she was hungry but she was not interested in food when she was offered it). You guessed it, I gave up! I also promised myself that I would have a shower every day when I was home with her, and I did, but I used to marvel at how low my standards of achievement had fallen.

Maybe because I was so housebound, and being an avid talker with no one to talk to but an infant and an old dog (who was less than impressed that this little bundle of noise and smells had arrived on the scene), I found that I started singing to myself a lot. Just to fill the void because *daytime television will rot your brain, people!* It helped a little every day and I often used to turn around to check on my daughter on her playmat while I was singing, and find her staring at me very intently.

It strikes me that I may have been self-medicating with singing. There are worse ways to do it, I guess. I wasn't aware why I was doing it or the impact it was having on me or my daughter, but it did help. I often find myself singing now when I am out in our vegetable garden. The veggie patch was an initiative I started when our daughter was young, mainly to create an activity we could all do outside and to teach her where her food came from. Little did I know it was also to feed my daughter's cherry tomato habit, which could have easily bankrupted us if we didn't grow them at home. Even now I am very aware of a tiny flicker in my emotional state when I seem to want to sing and I give myself permission to sing quietly to myself.

The science of what is happening is intriguing for three reasons. Firstly, to sing we need to take deeper breaths and take in more oxygen[63] than we do when we prepare to speak. Think of any yoga class you have attended or meditation podcast you have listened to, they all start with "take a deep breath in". Secondly, the hormone that is released when we sing is good old cortisol, otherwise known as our stress hormone. Singing returns our cortisol levels to normal, and in infants maternal singing has been found to both decrease cortisol levels if they were high (associated with stress) and increase them if they were low (associated with depression)[64]. Thirdly, if we are in a group, singing tends to encourage others to join in, which reinforces our social connections and gets those other happy hormones like endorphins and dopamine flowing again[65].

The trick is to notice when you get that little tickle in your throat or fleeting emotional desire to sing. What happens next? Do you dismiss it? Do you look around to see if anyone noticed you almost burst into song? Do you shake your head for entertaining such a silly notion? I wonder if it is your brain and body trying to help you self-medicate when things are not all sunshine and rainbows. True, most of the time in our modern world spontaneous singing isn't really the done thing. But imagine if it was?

Conclusion

There it is, *The Lullaby Effect* is done! Creative processes are always surprising. What you have read here is the second version of this book. The first one was all researcher-like and informative, and writing every word was like pulling blood from a stone. So I stopped and thought about what was really important to me. What emerged was that I wanted to share a little bit of what I think is fascinating research with you and how I came to understand and use it.

To pull all the elements you have read about in this book together, this is what we have come to understand about music and sound and your baby's/toddler's brain:

- At birth, babies understand their mother's voice using their music-processing network.
- Your baby's auditory-processing network (and yours too for that matter) are the largest gatherers of information among your senses – and they never turn off.
- Learning how to communicate using language is predicated by learning how to distinguish speech from all other sounds and then hear the tiny differences within speech.
- Babies use music, specifically musical beat, to teach their bodies how to move with intention and control.

- Singing contains more emotional content than speech.
- Your baby identifies you firstly through the unique tone colour of your voice.
- Singing to and moving in time with your baby helps them feel connected to you and empathic towards others they move and sing with.
- Your voice is your baby's favourite sound.

Raising a child, even the second and third time around (or as a grandparent) is a new adventure. Each child is different and comes to understand their world in their own way. As a parent, it is a "choose your own adventure" every time around.

I have shared more of myself in this book than I ever thought I would, but I've also kept to the rule that there is nothing in this book that I wouldn't say at a presentation, or in an interview, or directly to you, my dear reader. This was my journey into being a parent and to following a passion that is important to me in so many ways.

I'll leave you with this:

You have a voice and you can sing. You have a child (or grandchild) and they *need* you to sing. Cast aside those damaging ideas that you can't sing or that you aren't musical. We are all musical because we are all human. Hum a little tune, I dare you!

Thanks

This book, like most of my life, has been an experiment. I wanted to share all this amazing research that I found, but I wanted it to be outside of the world of academia and peer-reviewed judgement. Yet strangely, without the scrutiny and, ultimately, permission that the peer-review process gives you, I felt a little lost as to how to make *The Lullaby Effect* become an actual 'thing'.

For that reason, I want to thank my dear friends Steve Shann, Janet Smith, Julia Atkin, Susan de Weger and Neryl Jeanneret, who straddled the academic and "real" world, who encouraged me to keep experimenting, and had more belief than I that this process would work. I would also like to thank the experts around the world who ensured that in the translation of the research, I maintained the integrity of their work, including Jessica Mclean and Laura Cirelli.

The title for the book and the actual idea came from a serendipitous meeting with the brilliant radio producer Shevonne Hunt from Kinderling Kids Radio. I knew I wanted to share my passion and ideas, but working with her on the podcast series and being embraced by the Kinderling family gave me confidence and purpose to get skating across the keys and write this book. My thanks also go to Pepita Oliver for her beautiful butterfly logo and to my dear friend Lucas

Edmonds who is always there for me in life and in any graphic design crisis.

A different kind of confidence and purpose came from the many baristas who sustained me with great coffee throughout the writing process, and the proprietors who allowed me to sit for longer than a standard coffee time in their cafés. There were many, but I want to thank my locals – Tilley Devine's Café, Knox Made in Watson and Edgar's Inn.

Without the tried-and-true avenues of peer review, I had to find my own review panel. I looked to my trusted friends Karen Gabbott, Meagan Pearse, Janet Smith, Susan de Weger, Kellie Ryan, Rachael Dwyer and Tina Harris for feedback and support. You are altogether brilliant ladies!

Last, as always, but not least, thanks to my husband and partner in creative and crazy crime – and the real hero of my body and baby brain years – M.

The research

Chapter 1

[1] Thompson, W. F., Schellenberg, E. G., & Husain, G. (2001). Arousal, mood, and the Mozart effect. *Psychological science, 12*(3), 248–251.

[2] Steele, K. M., Bass, K. E., & Crook, M. D. (1999). The mystery of the Mozart effect: Failure to replicate. *Psychological Science, 10*(4), 366–369.

[3] Nantais, K. M., & Schellenberg, E. G. (1999). The Mozart effect: An artifact of preference. *Psychological Science, 10*(4), 370–373.

[4] Sound Health: Music and the Mind—Music and Childhood Development http://www.kennedy-center.org/calendar/event/NRMHB

[5] Peretz, I. (2015). WOMB TO TOMB. *Singing and Wellbeing: Ancient Wisdom, Modern Proof*, 42.

[6] Trainor, L. J., Austin, C. M., & Desjardins, R. N. (2000). Is infant-directed speech prosody a result of the vocal expression of emotion? *Psychological science, 11*(3), 188–195.

[7] Is Musical, E. C. (2016). Infant Musicality. *The Oxford Handbook of Music Psychology*, 387.

[8] Ramírez-Esparza, N., García-Sierra, A., & Kuhl, P. K. (2014). Look who's talking: speech style and social context in language input to infants are linked to concurrent and future speech development. *Developmental science, 17*(6), 880–891.

[9] Hannon, E. E., Lévêque, Y., Nave, K. M., & Trehub, S. E. (2016). Exaggeration of Language-Specific Rhythms in English and French Children's Songs. *Frontiers in psychology*, 7.

[10] Gold, B., Morgan, N., & Ellis, D. (2011). *Speech and audio signal processing: processing and perception of speech and music*. John Wiley & Sons.

[11] Trehub, S. E., Ghazban, N., & Corbeil, M. (2015). Musical affect regulation in infancy. *Annals of the New York Academy of Sciences*, *1337*(1), 186–192.

[12] Barrett, M. S. (2009). Sounding lives in and through music: a narrative inquiry of the everyday musical engagement of a young child. *Journal of Early Childhood Research*, *7*(2), 115–134.

Chapter 2

[13] Weis, D. Y. (2006). *Impact of Parent-Child Mother Goose: mothers' perceptions and experiences of singing to their infants aged 6–28 months* (Doctoral dissertation).

[14] Cirelli, L.K.*, Jurewicz, Z.B., & Trehub, S.E. (2017, July). Behavioral and physiological responses to maternal lullabies and play songs. Paper presented at the Society for Music Perception and Cognition Conference, San Diego, CA.

[15] Nakata, T., & Trehub, S. E. (2004). Infants' responsiveness to maternal speech and singing. *Infant Behavior and Development*, *27*(4), 455–464.

[16] Peretz, I. (2006). The nature of music from a biological perspective. *Cognition*, *100*(1), 1–32.

[17] Trehub, S. E., & Hannon, E. E. (2006). Infant music perception: Domain-general or domain-specific mechanisms?. *Cognition*, *100*(1), 73–99.

Chapter 3

[18] Chen, J. L., Penhune, V. B., & Zatorre, R. J. (2008). Moving on time: brain network for auditory-motor synchronization is modulated by rhythm complexity and musical training. *Journal of cognitive neuroscience*, *20*(2), 226–239.

[19] Furuya, S., Klaus, M., Nitsche, M.A., Paulus, W. and Altenmüller, E. (2014a). Ceiling effects prevent further improvement of transcranial stimulation in skilled musicians. Journal of Neuroscience. *34,* 13834–13839.

[20] Tang, Y. Y., Ma, Y., Wang, J., Fan, Y., Feng, S., Lu, Q., ... & Posner, M. I. (2007). Short-term meditation training improves attention and self-regulation. *Proceedings of the National Academy of Sciences*, *104*(43), 17152–17156.

[21] Van den Tol, A. J., & Edwards, J. (2015). Listening to sad music in adverse situations: How music selection strategies relate to self-regulatory goals, listening effects, and mood enhancement. *Psychology of Music*, *43*(4), 473–494.

[22] Waber, D. P., Weiler, M. D., Bellinger, D. C., Marcus, D. J., Forbes, P. W., Wypij, D., & Wolff, P. H. (2000). Diminished motor timing control in children referred for diagnosis of learning problems. *Developmental neuropsychology*, *17*(2), 181–197.

[23] Seither-Preisler, A., Parncutt, R., & Schneider, P. (2014). Size and synchronization of auditory cortex promotes musical, literacy, and attentional skills in children. *Journal of Neuroscience*, *34*(33), 10937–10949.

[24] Carr, K. W., White-Schwoch, T., Tierney, A. T., Strait, D. L., & Kraus, N. (2014). Beat synchronization predicts neural speech encoding and reading readiness in preschoolers. *Proceedings of the National Academy of Sciences*, *111*(40), 14559–14564.

[25] Tierney, A. T., & Kraus, N. (2013). The ability to tap to a beat relates to cognitive, linguistic, and perceptual skills. *Brain and language*, *124*(3), 225–231.

[26] Corrigall, K. A., & Trainor, L. J. (2011). Associations between length of music training and reading skills in children. *Music Perception: An Interdisciplinary Journal*, *29*(2), 147–155.

[27] Gordon, R. L., Shivers, C. M., Wieland, E. A., Kotz, S. A., Yoder, P. J., & Devin McAuley, J. (2015). Musical rhythm discrimination explains individual differences in grammar skills in children. *Developmental Science*, *18*(4), 635–644.

[28] Hansen, D., Bernstorf, E., & Stuber, G. M. (2014). *The music and literacy connection*. Rowman & Littlefield.

[29] Wiggins, D. G. (2007). Pre-K music and the emergent reader: Promoting literacy in a music-enhanced environment. *Early Childhood Education Journal*, *35*(1), 55–64.

Chapter 4

[30] Schön, D., Magne, C., & Besson, M. (2004). The music of speech: Music training facilitates pitch processing in both music and language. *Psychophysiology*, *41*(3), 341–349.

[31] Brown, S., Martinez, M. J., & Parsons, L. M. (2006). Music and language side by side in the brain: a PET study of the generation of melodies and sentences. *European journal of neuroscience*, *23*(10), 2791–2803.

[32] Strait, D. L., Parbery-Clark, A., Hittner, E., & Kraus, N. (2012). Musical training during early childhood enhances the neural encoding of speech in noise. *Brain and language*, *123*(3), 191–201.

[33] Abrams, D. A., Nicol, T., Zecker, S., & Kraus, N. (2009). Abnormal cortical processing of the syllable rate of speech in poor readers. *Journal of Neuroscience*, *29*(24), 7686–7693.

[34] Patel, A. D. (2014). Can nonlinguistic musical training change the way the brain processes speech? The expanded OPERA hypothesis. *Hearing research, 308*, 98–108.

[35] Peppé, S., Cleland, J., Gibbon, F., O'Hare, A., & Castilla, P. M. (2011). Expressive prosody in children with autism spectrum conditions. *Journal of Neurolinguistics, 24*(1), 41–53.

[36] Perani, D., Saccuman, M. C., Scifo, P., Spada, D., Andreolli, G., Rovelli, R., Baldoli, C. & Koelsch, S. (2010). Functional specializations for music processing in the human newborn brain. *Proceedings of the National Academy of Sciences, 107*(10), 4758–4763.

[37] Hart, B., & Risley, T. R. (2003). The early catastrophe: The 30 million word gap by age 3. *American educator, 27*(1), 4–9.

[38] Kraus, N., & White-Schwoch, T. (2017). Neurobiology of Everyday Communication: What Have We Learned From Music?. *The Neuroscientist, 23*(3), 287–298.

[39] Besson, M., Schön, D., Moreno, S., Santos, A., & Magne, C. (2007). Influence of musical expertise and musical training on pitch processing in music and language. *Restorative neurology and neuroscience, 25*(3–4), 399–410.

Chapter 5

[40] Cirelli, L. K., Wan, S. J., & Trainor, L. J. (2016). Social effects of movement synchrony: increased infant helpfulness only transfers to affiliates of synchronously moving partners. *Infancy, 21*(6), 807–821.

[41] Cirelli, L. K., Wan, S. J., & Trainor, L. J. (2014). Fourteen-month-old infants use interpersonal synchrony as a cue to direct helpfulness. *Phil. Trans. R. Soc. B, 369*(1658), 20130400.

[42] Kirschner, S., & Tomasello, M. (2010). Joint music making promotes prosocial behavior in 4-year-old children. *Evolution and Human Behavior, 31*(5), 354–364.

[43] Cirelli, L. K., Wan, S. J., & Trainor, L. J. (2014). Fourteen-month-old infants use interpersonal synchrony as a cue to direct helpfulness. *Phil. Trans. R. Soc. B*, *369*(1658), 20130400.

[44] Cirelli, L. K., Wan, S. J., & Trainor, L. J. (2014). Fourteen-month-old infants use interpersonal synchrony as a cue to direct helpfulness. *Phil. Trans. R. Soc. B*, *369*(1658), 20130400.

[45] Swaminathan, S., & Schellenberg, E. G. (2016). Music training. In *Cognitive Training* (pp. 137–144). Springer International Publishing.

Chapter 6

[46] Henriksson-Macaulay, L. (2014). *The Music Miracle: The Scientific Secret to Unlocking Your Child's Full Potential*. Earnest House Publishing.

[47] Levitin, D. (2006), This Is Your Brain On Music. Penguin.

[48] Collins, A. (2013). Neuroscience meets music education: Exploring the implications of neural processing models on music education practice. *International Journal of Music Education*, *31*(2), 217–231.

[49] Robinson, K. (2011). *Out of our minds: Learning to be creative*. John Wiley & Sons.

[50] Levitin, D. (2016). *A Field Guide to Lies and Statistics: A Neuroscientist on How to Make Sense of a Complex World*. Penguin UK.

Chapter 7

[51] Reimer, B. (2009). *Seeking the significance of music education: Essays and reflections*. R&L Education.

[52] Patel, A. D. (2010). Music, biological evolution, and the brain. *Emerging disciplines*, 91–144.

[53] Morley, I. (2013). *The prehistory of music: human evolution, archaeology, and the origins of musicality*. Oxford University Press.

[54] Mithen, S., Morley, I., Wray, A., Tallerman, M., & Gamble, C. (2006). The Singing Neanderthals: the Origins of Music, Language, Mind and Body, by Steven Mithen. London: Weidenfeld & Nicholson, 2005.

[55] Fitch, W. T. (2006). The biology and evolution of music: A comparative perspective. *Cognition*, *100*(1), 173–215.

[56] Trainor, L. J. (2006). Innateness, learning, and the difficulty of determining whether music is an evolutionary adaptation. *Music Perception: An Interdisciplinary Journal*, *24*(1), 105–110.

[57] Clift, S., Hancox, G., Morrison, I., Hess, B., Kreutz, G., & Stewart, D. (2010). Choral singing and psychological wellbeing: Quantitative and qualitative findings from English choirs in a cross-national survey. *Journal of Applied Arts & Health*, *1*(1), 19–34.

[58] Norton, K. (2015). *Singing and wellbeing: Ancient wisdom, modern proof*. Routledge.

[59] MacDonald, R., Kreutz, G., & Mitchell, L. (Eds.). (2013). *Music, health, and wellbeing*. Oxford University Press.

[60] Field, T. (2010). Postpartum depression effects on early interactions, parenting, and safety practices: a review. *Infant Behavior and Development*, *33*(1), 1–6.

[61] Mackinlay, E., & Baker, F. (2005). Nurturing herself, nurturing her baby: Creating positive experiences for first-time mothers through lullaby singing. *Women and Music: A Journal of Gender and Culture*, *9*(1), 69–89.

[62] Trehub, S. E., Ghazban, N., & Corbeil, M. (2015). Musical affect regulation in infancy. *Annals of the New York Academy of Sciences*, *1337*(1), 186–192.

[63] Loewy, J., Stewart, K., Dassler, A. M., Telsey, A., & Homel, P. (2013). The effects of music therapy on vital signs, feeding, and sleep in premature infants. *Pediatrics*, *131*(5), 902–918.

[64] Shenfield, T., Trehub, S. E., & Nakata, T. (2003). Maternal singing modulates infant arousal. *Psychology of Music*, *31*(4), 365–375.

[65] Boso, M., Politi, P., Barale, F., & Emanuele, E. (2006). Neurophysiology and neurobiology of the musical experience. *Functional neurology*, *21*(4), 187.

Lightning Source UK Ltd.
Milton Keynes UK
UKHW02f0806221018
330964UK00016B/1084/P